THE SCREEN THIEF!

Story by
Helen Docherty

Illustrated by
Thomas Docherty

The Snaffle arrived in the city one day.
She wanted to make some new friends,
and to play.

But nobody realised the Snaffle was there.
The people she saw seemed too busy to care;
Everyone seemed to be glued to a screen.

The Snaffle was puzzled.
What *could* these screens mean?

What was so special?
What did they hide?

Perhaps they had some kind
of magic inside?

The Snaffle felt lonely,
all on her own.

Then she heard something beeping
– somebody's phone!

She sniffed it.

She bit it.

She chewed it;
    once,
        twice.

For something so shiny,
    it tasted . . . quite nice.

The Snaffle looked round her.
What else could she eat?
Some screens were salty,
And some screens were sweet.
There were screens you could nibble,
And screens you could munch,
Chewy screens, gooey screens,
Screens that went CRUNCH!

The Snaffle ate more and her appetite grew.
The tiniest phone screens would no longer do.
She polished off twenty computers
with ease,

And gobbled up fifty-nine widescreen TVs.

Cinemas started to turn folk away.
"Tonight's film is cancelled, we're sorry to say.
We don't know what's happened. It's ever so weird.
The seats are all there . . .

EXIT

but the screen's
disappeared!"

Adverts were swiped
from the city's main square.
People were left staring
into thin air.

Yet one child, called Max,
wasn't nearly so sad.
He didn't think life
without screens was that bad.

But nobody else was prepared to forgive.
"Without all our screens, how on earth can we live?"

A small, anxious crowd was beginning to grow.
"Who could have done this? Does anyone know?"

"I think that I saw her
- she's small, and she's blue!"

"She's sneaky!"
"And dangerous!"

"I saw her, too!"

The Snaffle sat down. She needed a break.
Her belly was full; it was starting to ache.
Despite all the various screens she had tried,
The Snaffle still felt kind of . . . empty, inside.

Then . . .

She saw
something different.
It somehow looked right:
A child playing happily
– no screen in sight!

She thought,
He looks friendly,
And Max thought
the same.

Two seconds later
she'd joined in his game!

Max and the Snaffle were laughing so loud,
Neither one noticed a large, angry crowd . . .

"Look! There's the monster that stole all our screens!"
"We can't let her near any other machines!"
"Stop her!" "Quick, catch her!"
"No! Chase her away!"

"Please don't!" Max protested. "She just wants to play! Why don't you all join us? It's really good fun."

Everyone stared . . .

– then joined in, one by one.

Things changed in the city, that same afternoon.
Screens were forgotten – surprisingly soon.
Folks chatted to neighbours; they played with their friends,
And discovered new ways to fill up their weekends.

And as for the Snaffle? She's never looked back . . .

. . . Though sometimes she snaffles a screen – for a snack.

For Owen, Lewis, Isla and Leo

First published in the UK in 2021 by Alison Green Books

An imprint of Scholastic Children's Books
Euston House, 24 Eversholt Street, London NW1 1DB
A division of Scholastic Ltd

www.scholastic.co.uk

London – New York – Toronto – Sydney – Auckland
Mexico City – New Delhi – Hong Kong

Designed by Zoë Tucker

HB ISBN: 978 1 407199 14 6
PB ISBN: 978 1 407199 15 3

Printed in China

1 3 5 7 9 8 6 4 2